Musidoku

The Musical Sudoku

**44 puzzles to tickle and tackle
your musical brain cells**

**Composed by
Antony Kearns**

CONTENTS

Stainer & Bell

First published in 2007 by Stainer & Bell Limited
23 Gruneisen Road, London N3 1DZ

© 2007 Stainer & Bell Ltd

British Library Cataloguing-in-Publication Data
A catalogue record of this book is available from the British Library

ISBN 978 0 85249 897 2

Printed in Great Britain by Caligraving Limited

Introduction

Welcome to this book of Musidoku puzzles, a musical variation on the hugely popular Sudoku number-place puzzle.

The rules are simple: just complete the empty boxes in the grid so that every row, every column and every 3 x 3 box contains one of each of the following nine musical symbols:

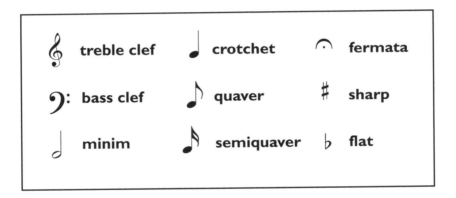

The puzzles become harder as you work your way through the book. To begin with there are a few very easy puzzles to get you tuned up before moving on to the *Moderato* examples. You can then proceed to greater heights with the *Rigoroso* études, in preparation for the *Virtuoso* level. Finally, four *Maestro* cadenzas prove the ultimate test for the elite Musidokist.

And don't forget to visit **www.musidoku.com** for a further fix of mind-twisting musical Sudoku puzzles.

1

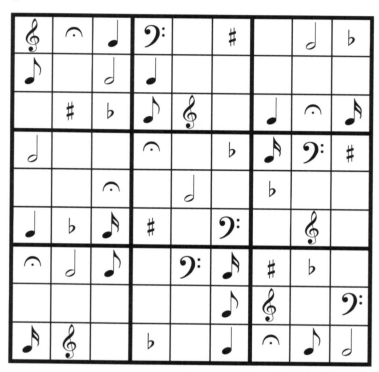

Symbols

2

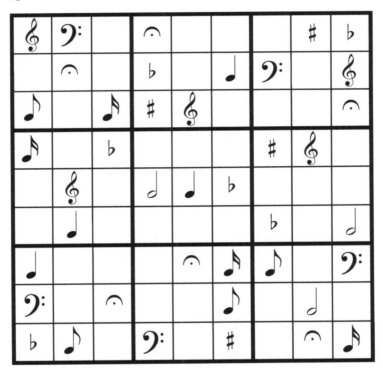

Symbols

3

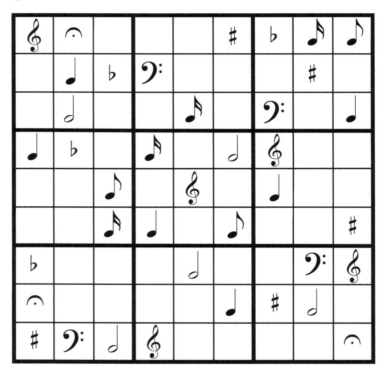

Symbols

4

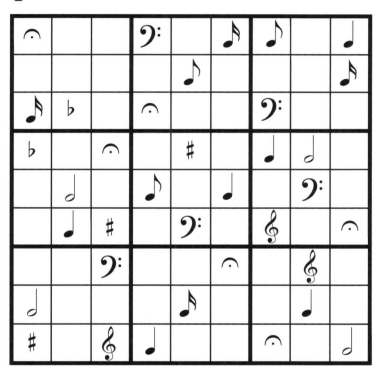

Symbols

5

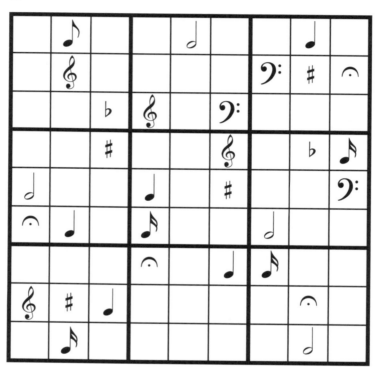

Symbols

6

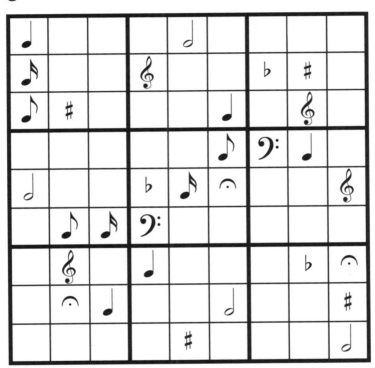

Symbols

7

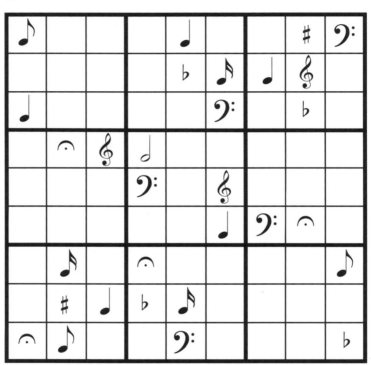

Symbols

8

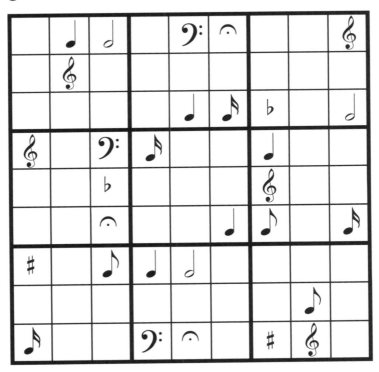

Symbols

Moderato

9

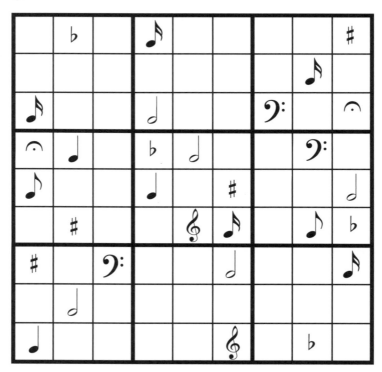

Symbols

10

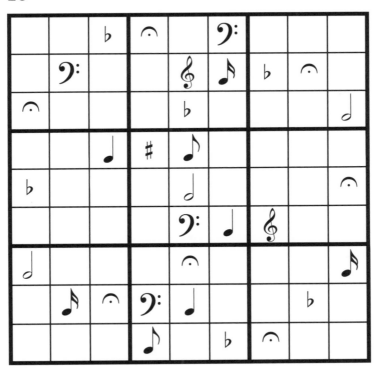

Symbols

11

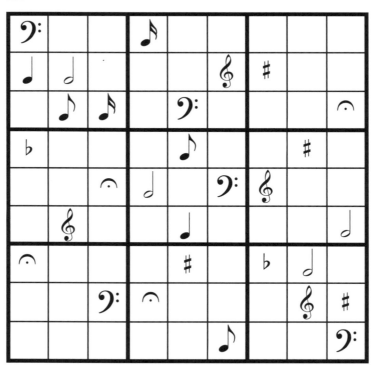

Symbols

12

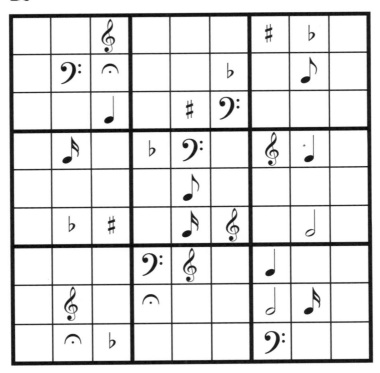

Symbols

13

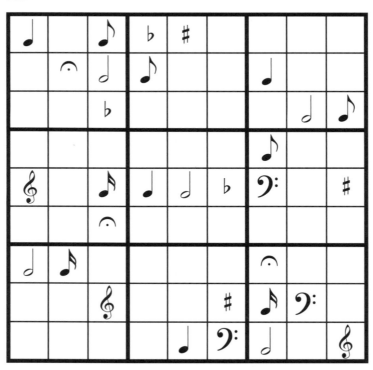

Symbols

14

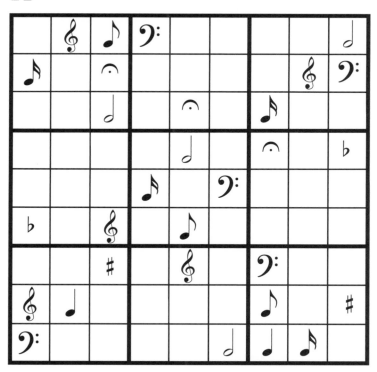

Symbols

15

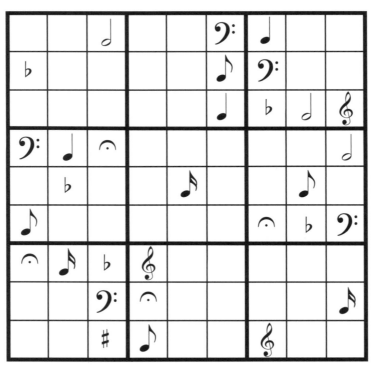

Symbols

16

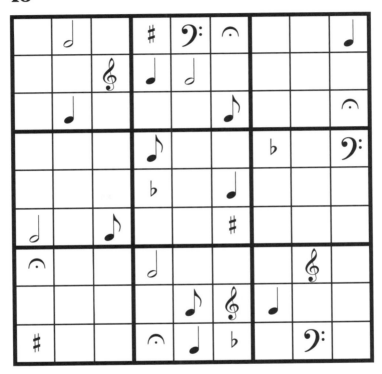

Symbols

17

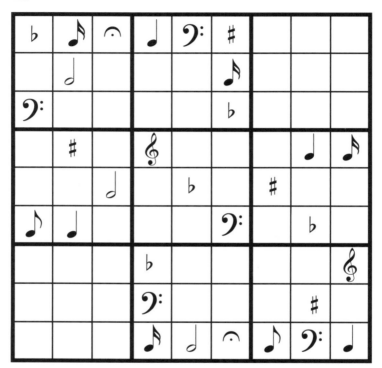

Symbols

18

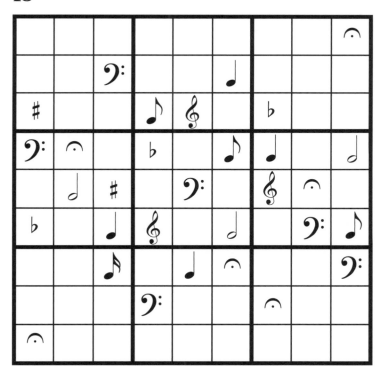

Symbols

19

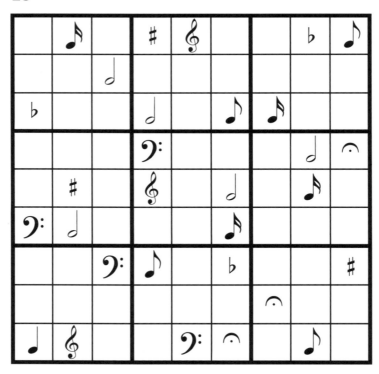

Symbols

20

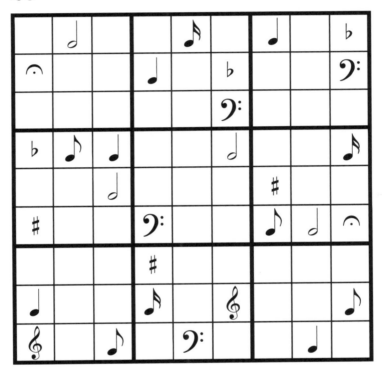

Symbols

21

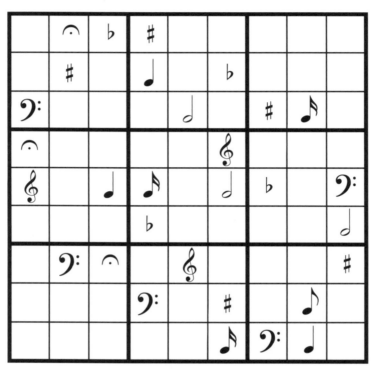

Symbols

22

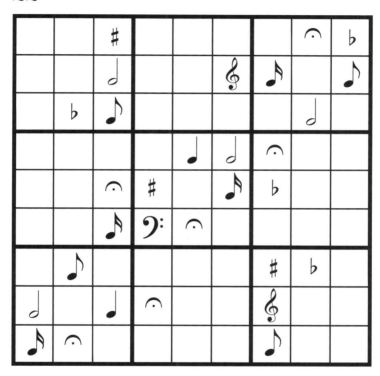

Symbols

23

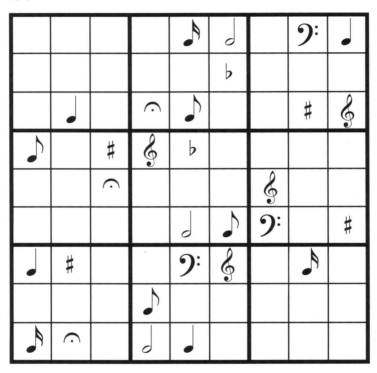

Symbols

24

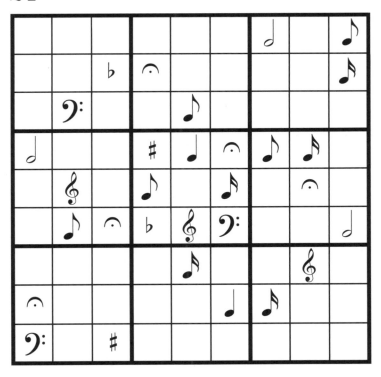

Symbols

25

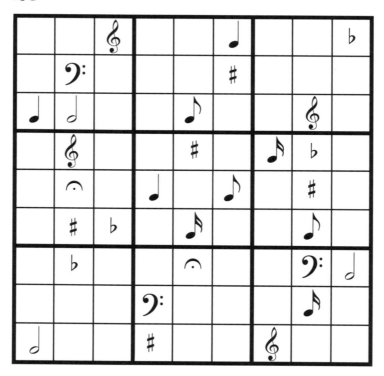

Symbols

26

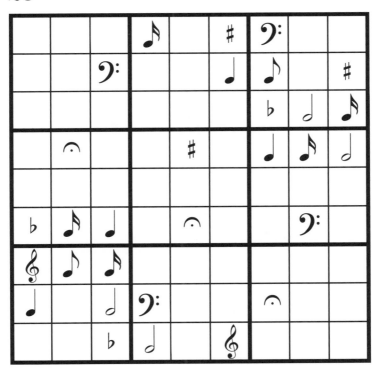

Symbols

27

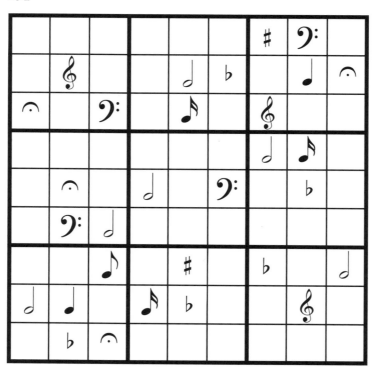

Symbols

28

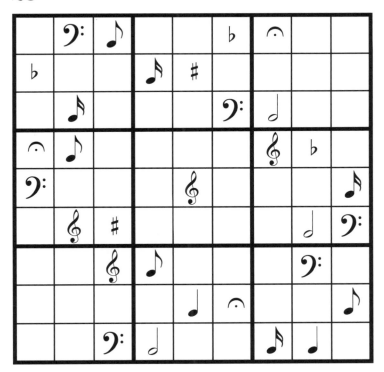

Symbols

29

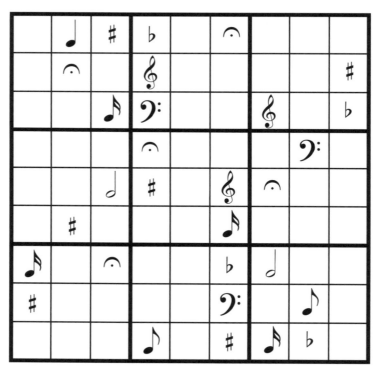

Symbols

30

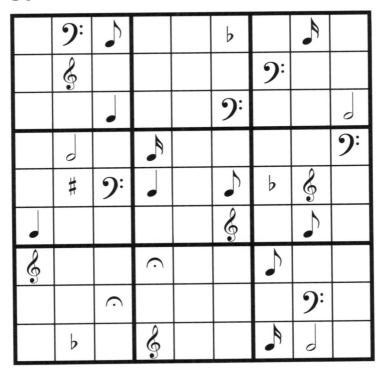

Symbols

31

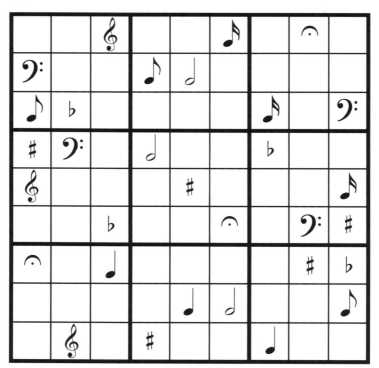

Symbols

32

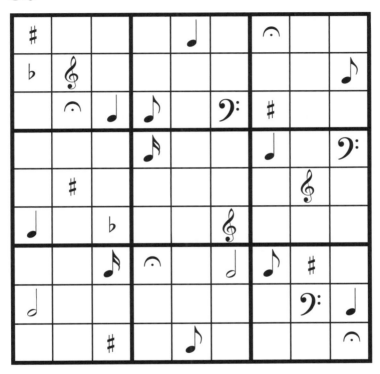

Symbols

33

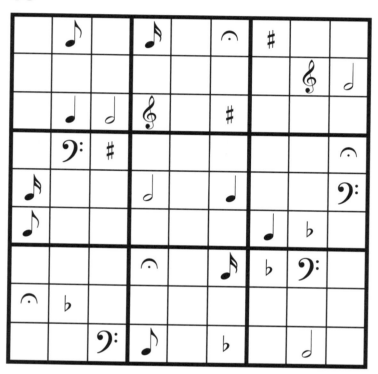

Symbols

34

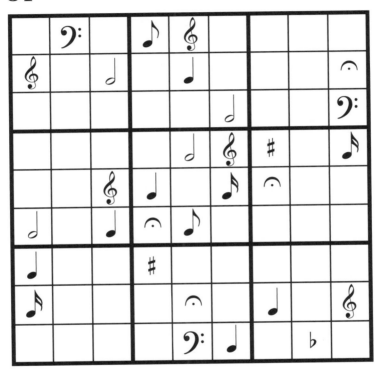

Symbols

35

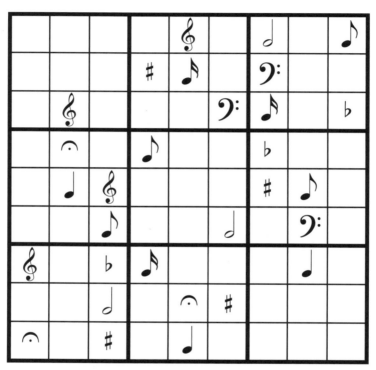

Symbols

36

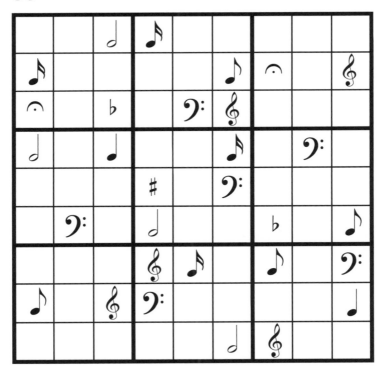

Symbols

37

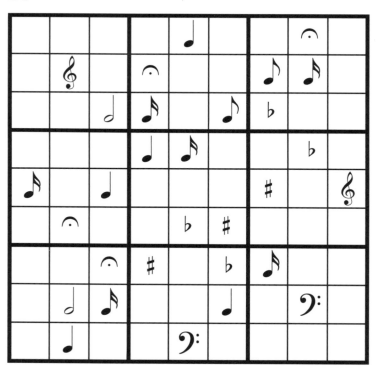

Symbols

38

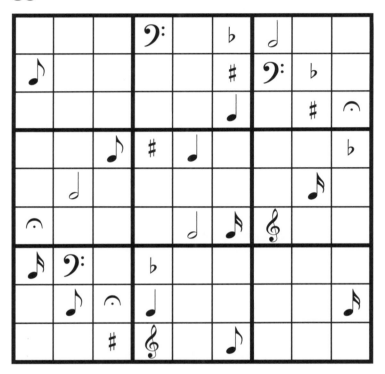

Symbols

39

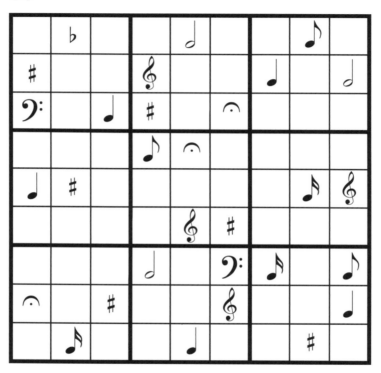

Symbols

40

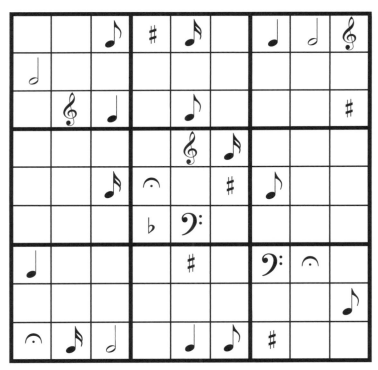

Symbols

41

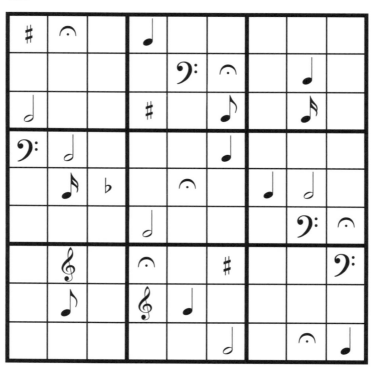

Symbols

42

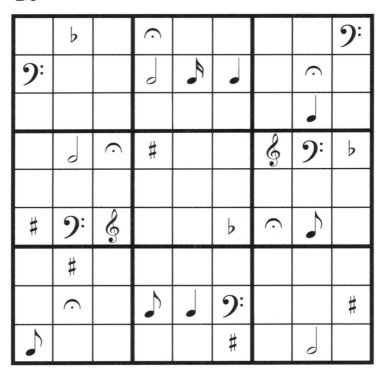

Symbols

43

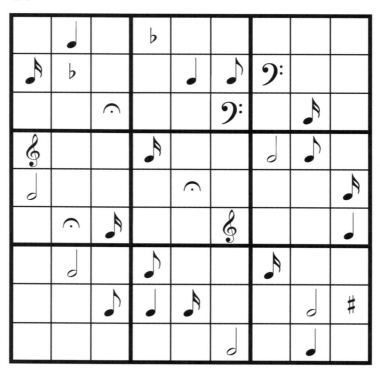

Symbols

44

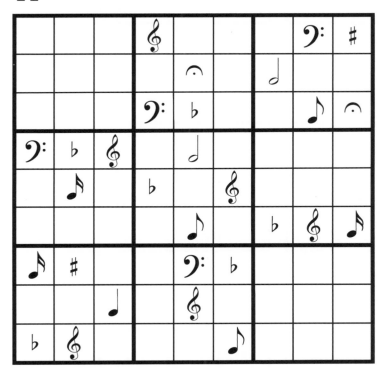

Symbols

Solutions

10

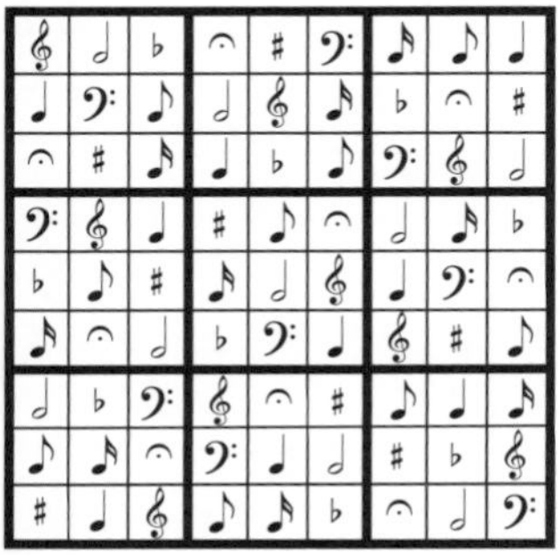

11

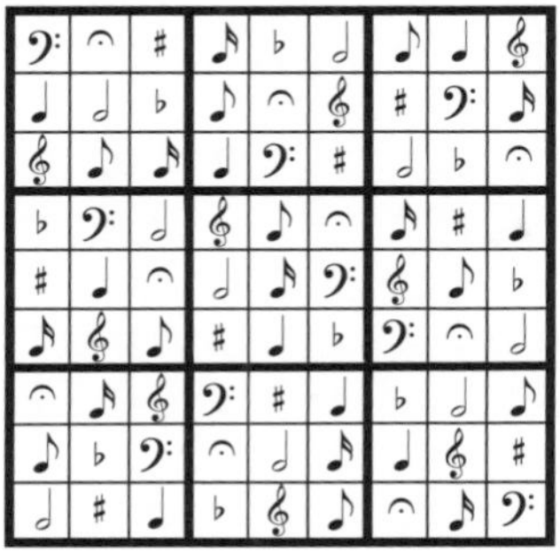

12

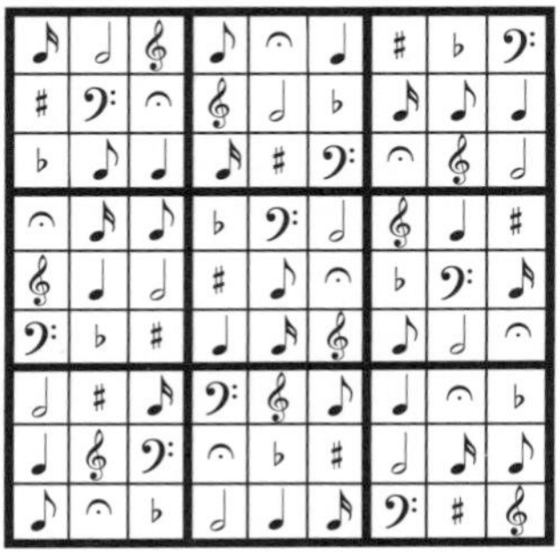

13

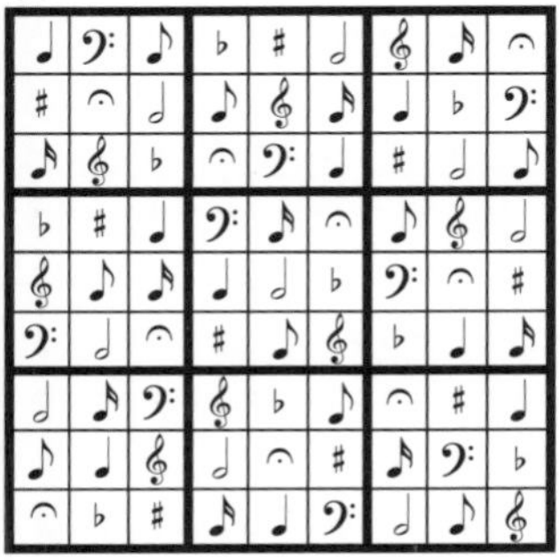

14

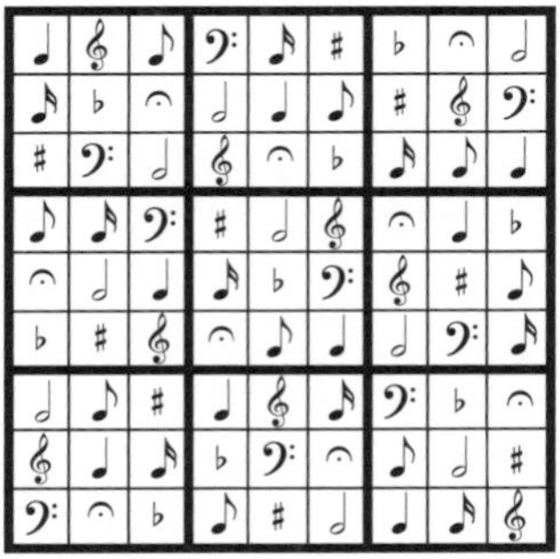

15

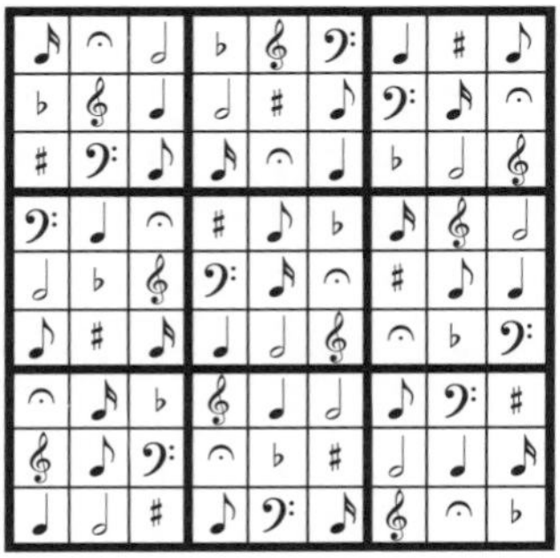

16

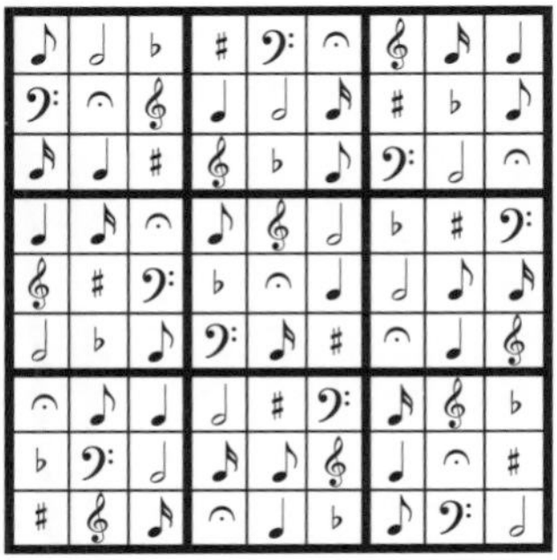

17

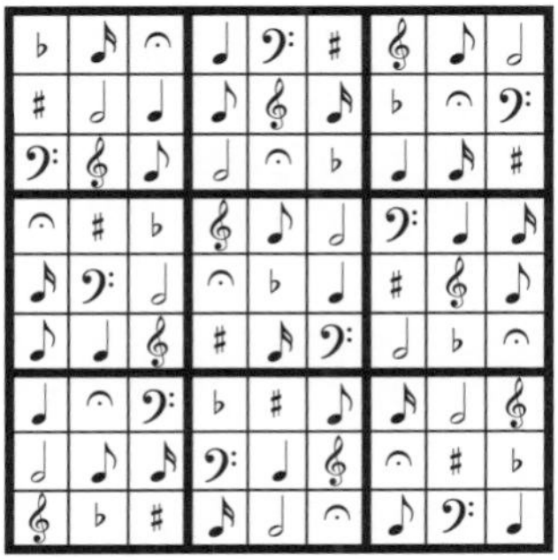

18

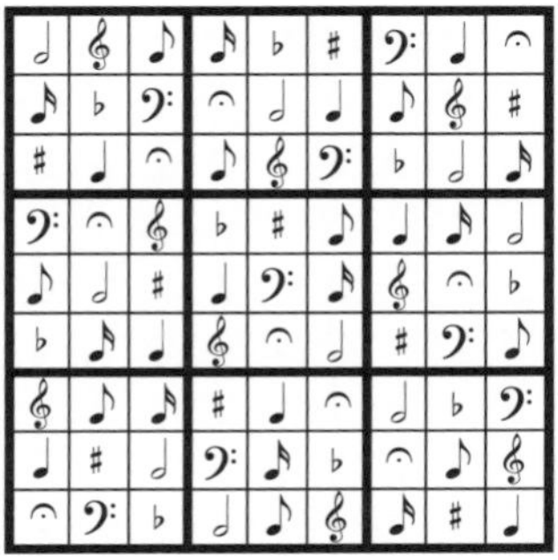

Solutions

19

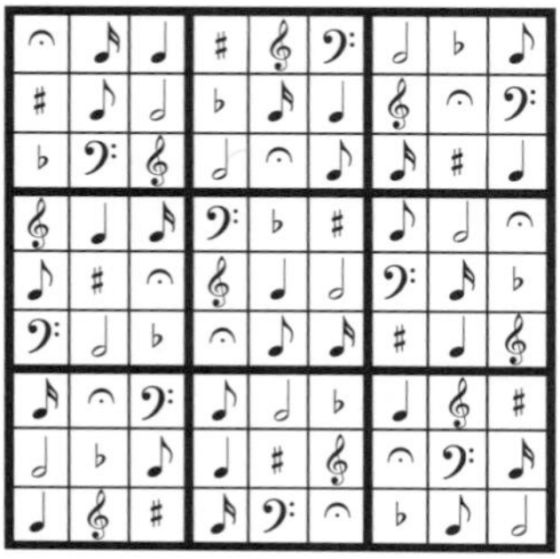

20

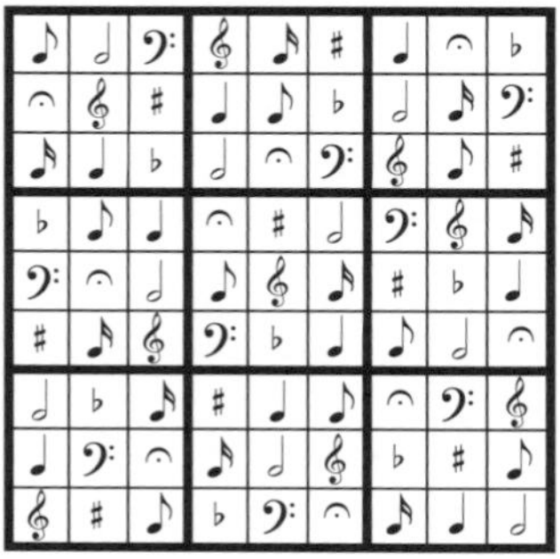

21

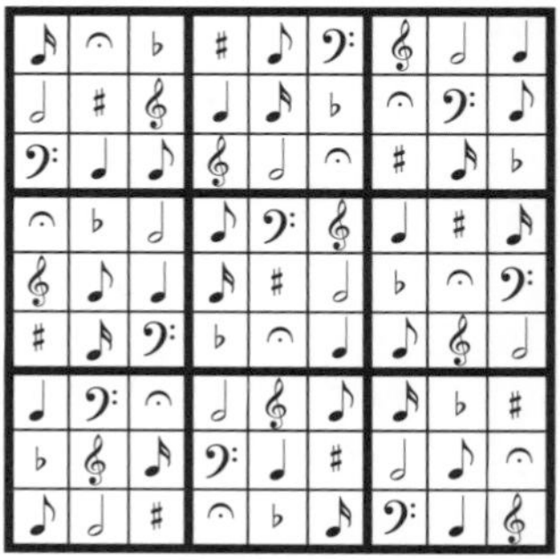

22

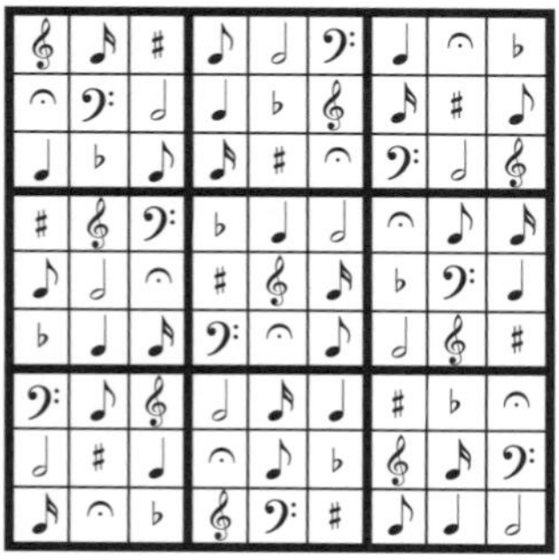

23

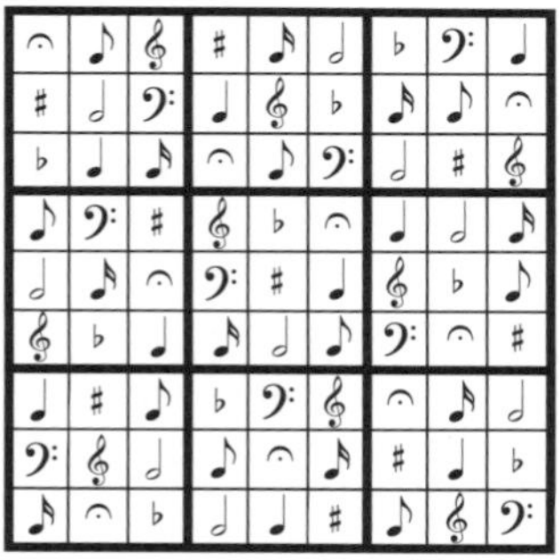

24

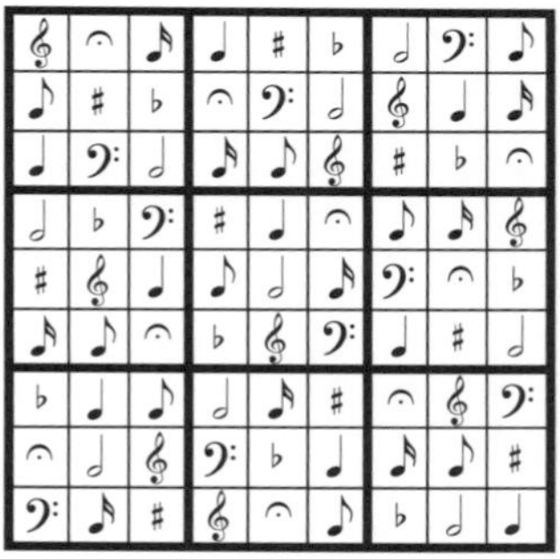

25

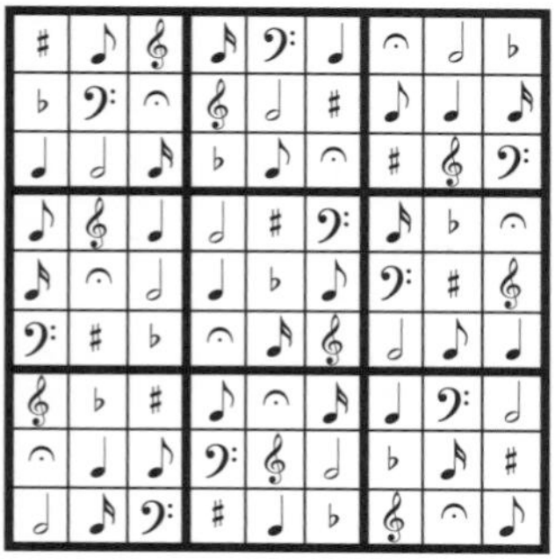

26

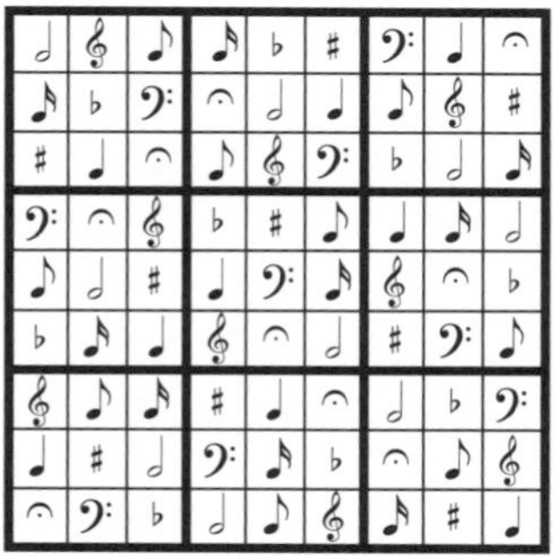

27

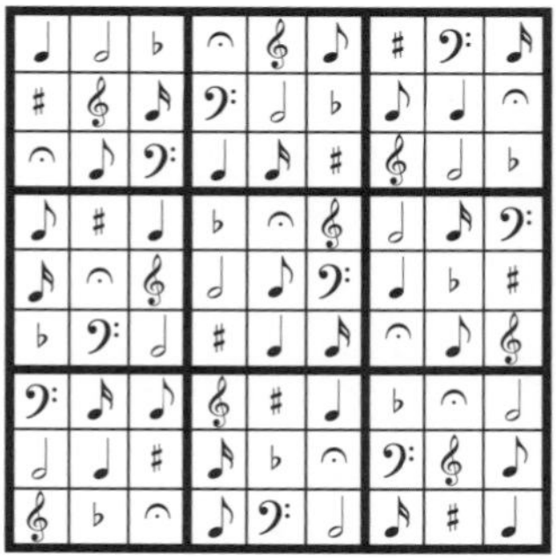

28

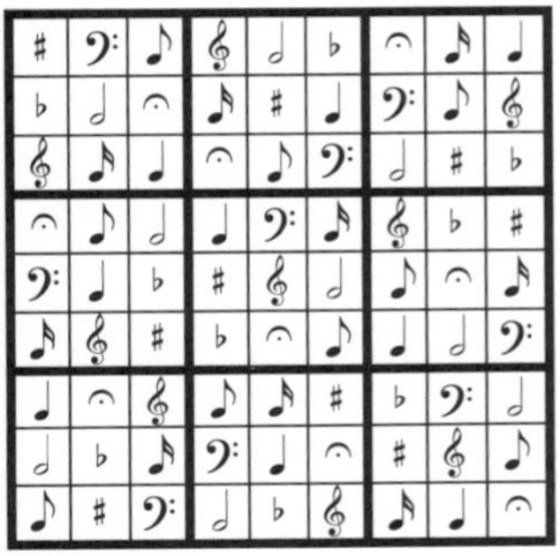

29

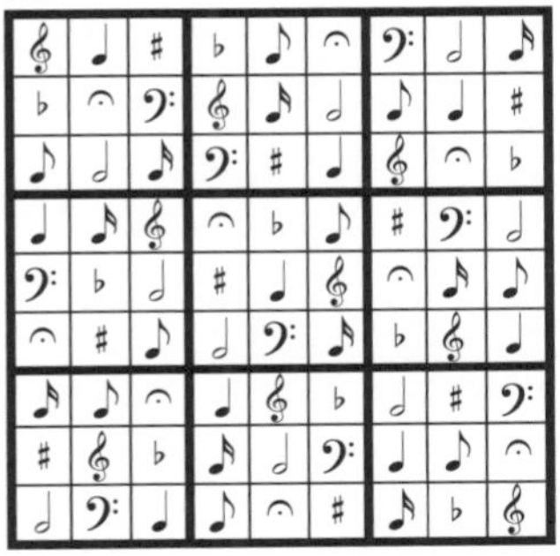

30

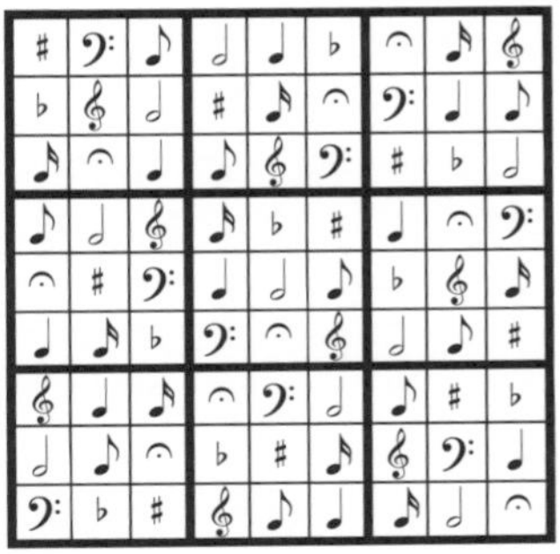

31

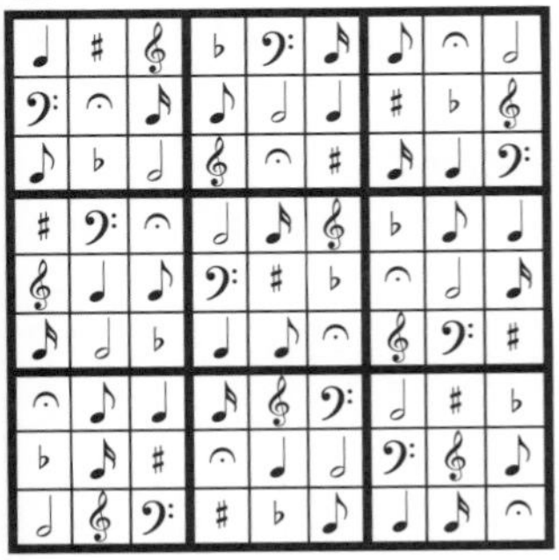

32

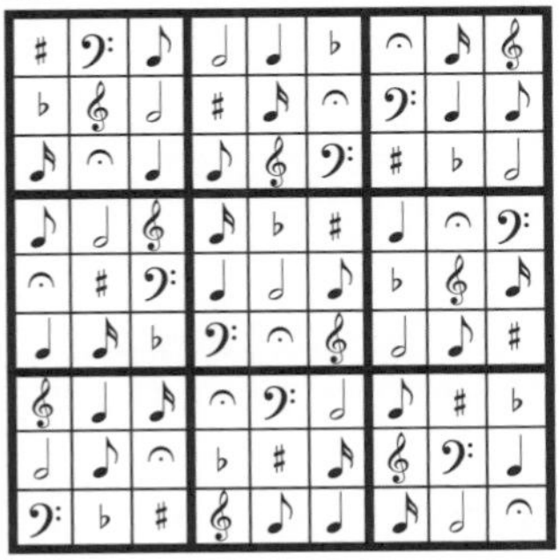

33

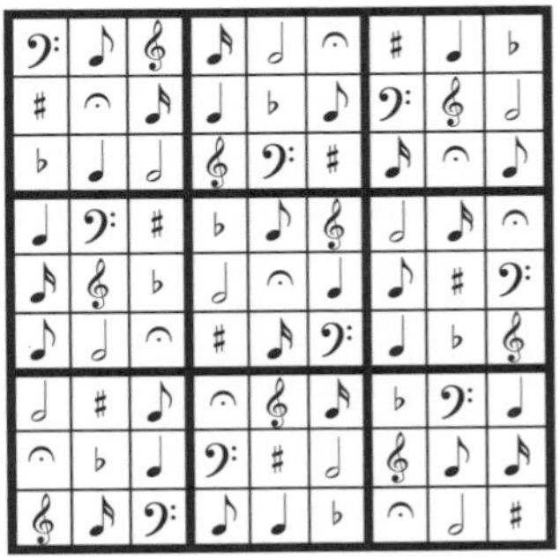

34

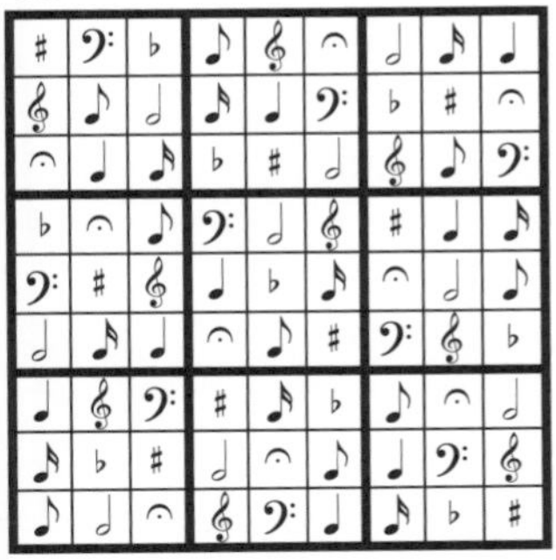

35

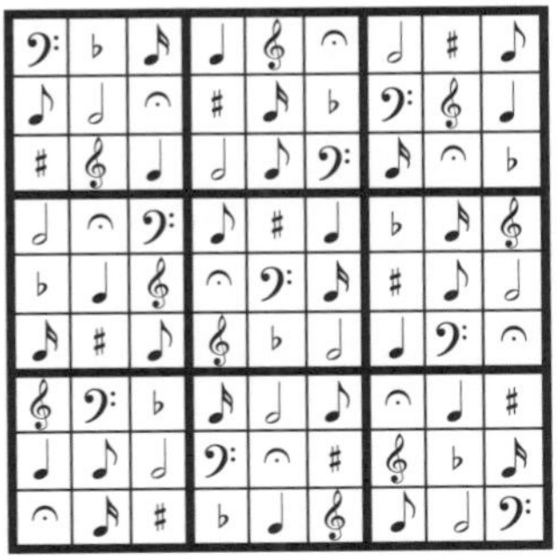

36

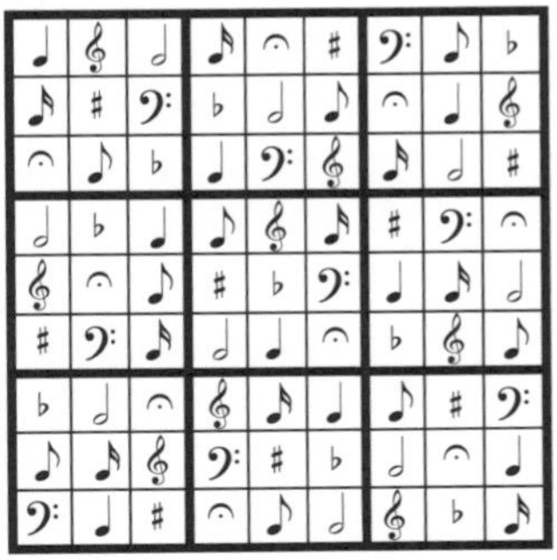

Solutions

37

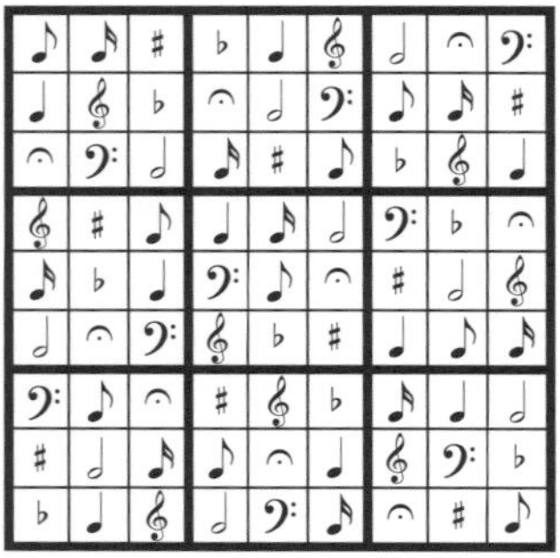

38

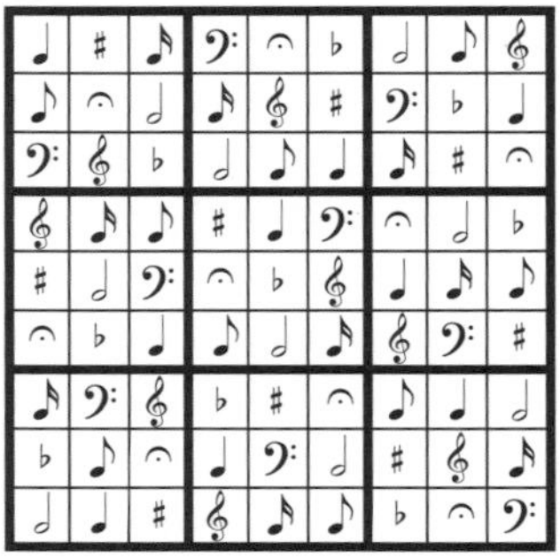

39

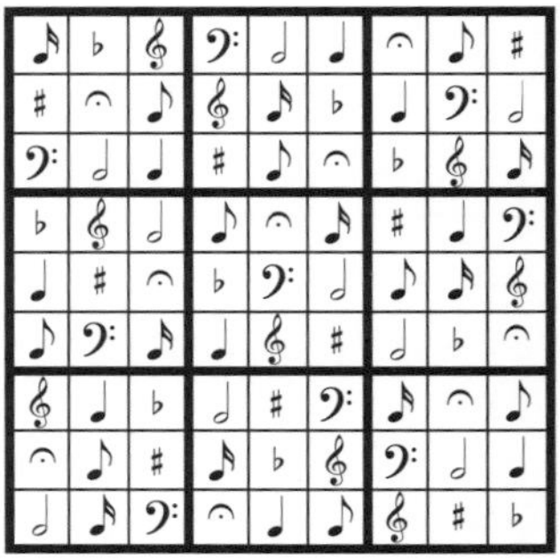

40

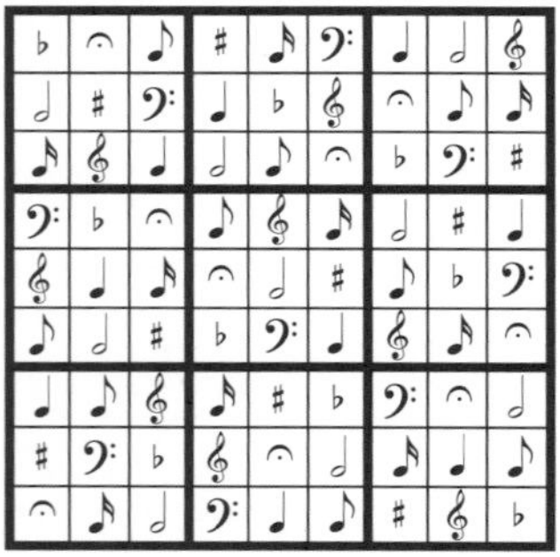

41

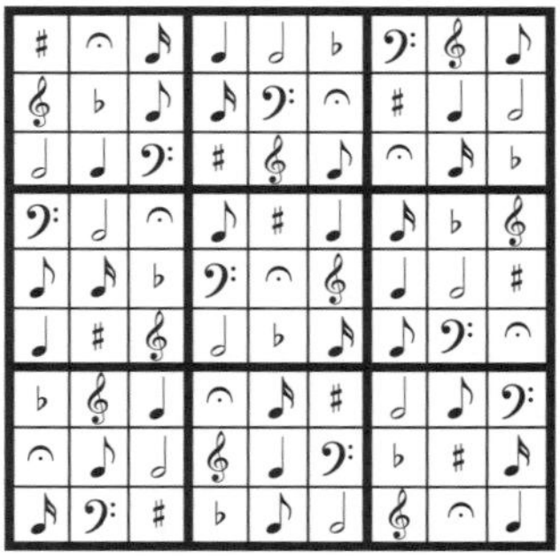

42

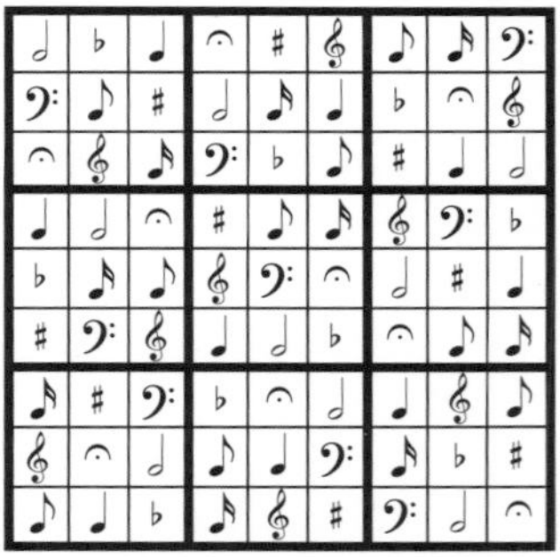

43

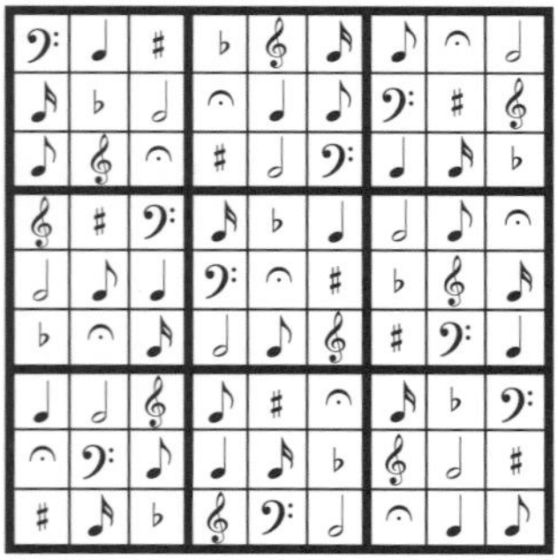

44

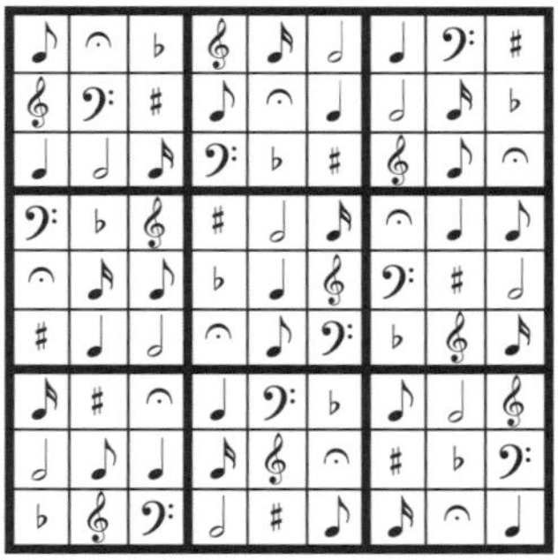